Maths BASICS

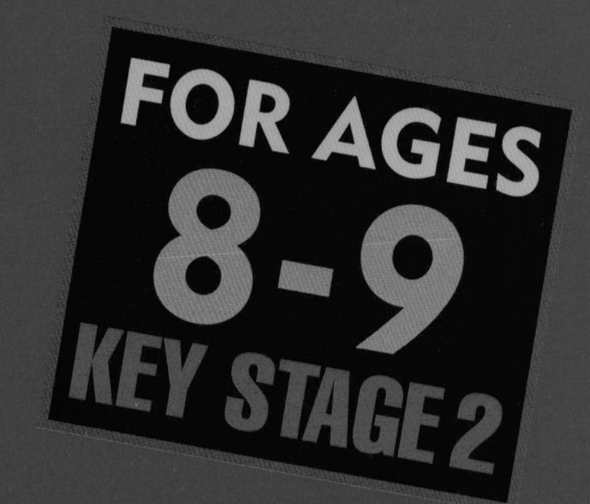

Contents

How to use this book

Numeracy Basics helps you to help your child practise many important basic skills covered in the *National Numeracy Strategy* and *National Curriculum*.

Each book is divided into *30 units* of work which focus on *one clear* objective.

Most of the units are designed using the same easy-to-follow *key features*. In some cases these features are combined into one activity, offering further practice where appropriate.

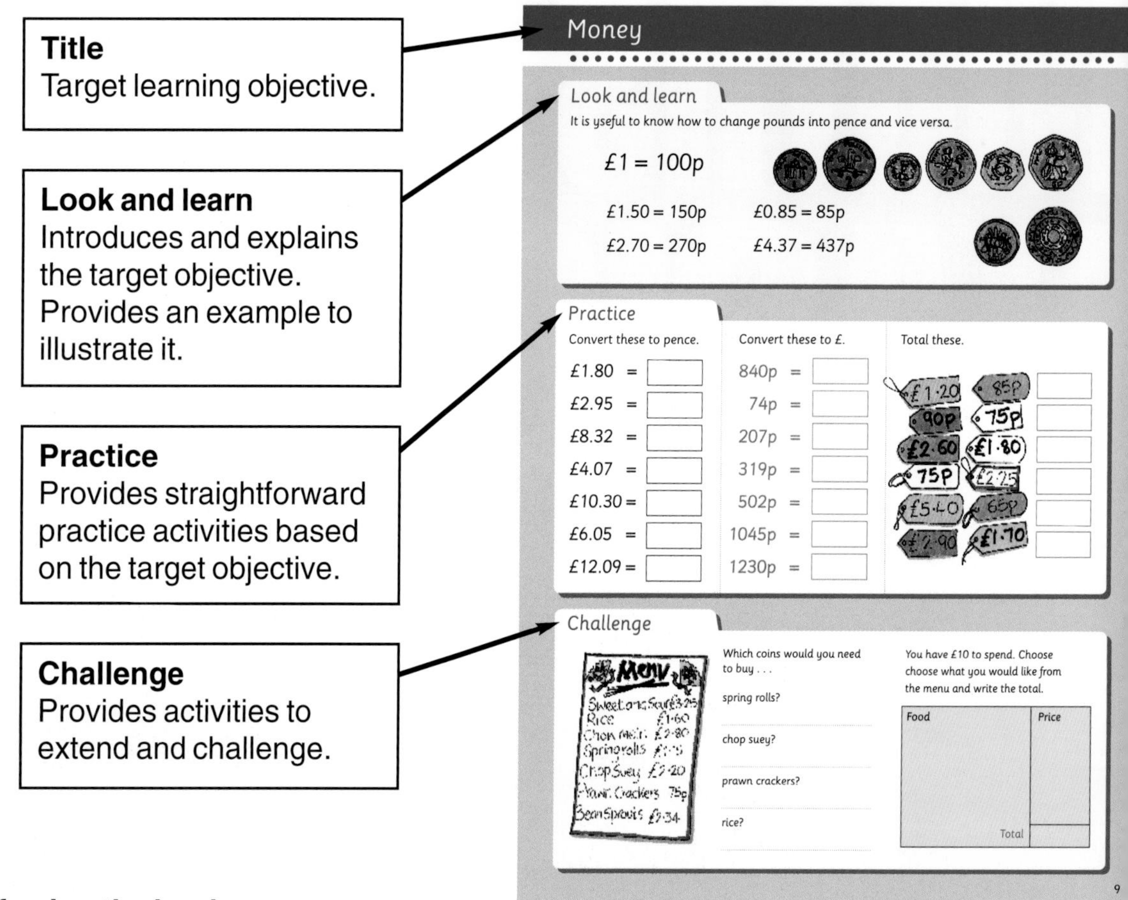

Suggested way of using the book

- It is suggested that your child works systematically through the book.
- Try tackling one unit per week.
- Read through and discuss the *Look and learn* section with your child to make sure the key objective is understood.
- Help your child get started on the Practice section.
- After this, your child can start to work fairly independently through the page, but will need further support and encouragement.
- The answers are supplied at the end of the book for checking each unit on its completion.

Enjoy the book!

Place value (1)

Look and learn

Each number is made from digits: 0, 1, 2, 3, 4, 5, 6, 7, 8 and 9.
The position of a digit in a number gives it a **value**.

thousands, hundreds, tens, units

6 2 8 7 = 6000 + 200 + 80 + 7

Practice

Write the missing numbers.

2386 = 2000 + ☐ + 80 + 6

4971 = ☐ + 900 + 70 + 1

8146 = 8000 + ☐ + ☐ + 6

2978 = ☐ + 900 + ☐ + ☐

5289 = ☐ + ☐ + 80 + ☐

6184 = ☐ + ☐ + ☐ + ☐

4719 = ☐ + ☐ + ☐ + ☐

Join the numbers to the words.

four thousand eight hundred	480
four hundred and eighty	8480
eight thousand and forty	4800
eight thousand and fourteen	8040
eight thousand four hundred and eighty	8014

Challenge

Rearrange these to make four-digit numbers: 6 8 3 9

Write as many four-digit numbers as you can.

Which is the largest?

Which is the smallest?

Addition and subtraction

Look and learn

Knowing number facts can help you to work out other calculations. Look at these patterns.

$8 + 3 = 11$	$14 - 9 = 5$
$80 + 30 = 110$	$140 - 90 = 50$
$800 + 300 = 1100$	$1400 - 900 = 500$

Practice

Fill in the missing numbers.

$7 + 5 =$ ☐

$70 + 50 =$ ☐

$700 + 500 =$ ☐

$9 + 6 =$ ☐

$90 + 60 =$ ☐

$900 + 600 =$ ☐

$4 + 11 =$ ☐

$40 + 110 =$ ☐

$400 + 1100 =$ ☐

Try these.

$13 - 6 =$ ☐

$130 - 60 =$ ☐

$1300 - 600 =$ ☐

$15 - 7 =$ ☐

$150 - 70 =$ ☐

$1500 - 700 =$ ☐

$18 - 9 =$ ☐

$180 - 90 =$ ☐

$1800 - 900 =$ ☐

Answer these.

$180 - 60 =$ ☐

$800 + 500 =$ ☐

$1700 - 400 =$ ☐

$1200 + 600 =$ ☐

$150 + 90 =$ ☐

$130 - 90 =$ ☐

$800 + 800 =$ ☐

Challenge

Write numbers to make these totals.

Measures

Look and learn

It is useful to remember equivalent measures.

1 centimetre = 10 millimetres
1cm = 10mm

1 kilometre = 1000 metres
1km = 1000m

1 litre = 1000 millilitres
1l = 1000ml

1 metre = 100 centimetres
1m = 100cm

1 kilogram = 1000 grams
1kg = 1000g

Practice

Answer these.

$\frac{1}{2}$ km = ☐ m

$\frac{1}{4}$ l = ☐ ml

$\frac{1}{4}$ m = ☐ cm

$\frac{1}{2}$ km = ☐ m

Use a ruler to measure these lines in millimetres.

a) .... mm

b) .... mm

c) .... mm

d) .... mm

e) .... mm

f) .... mm

Challenge

Find these objects. Estimate their weight, height or capacity. Check them by measuring.

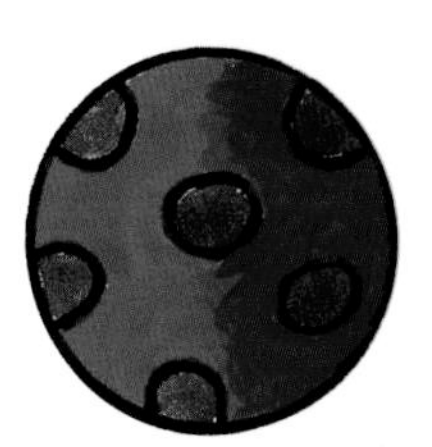

	estimate	measure
Weight of a ball		
Height of a person		
Capacity of a cereal bowl		

2D shapes

Look and learn

A polygon is any 2D shape with straight sides.
A regular polygon's sides and angles are all equal.

	triangle	quadrilateral	pentagon	hexagon	heptagon	octagon	nonagon	decagon
name of polygon								
number of sides	3	4	5	6	7	8	9	10

Practice

Name each shape, then tick all the right angles.

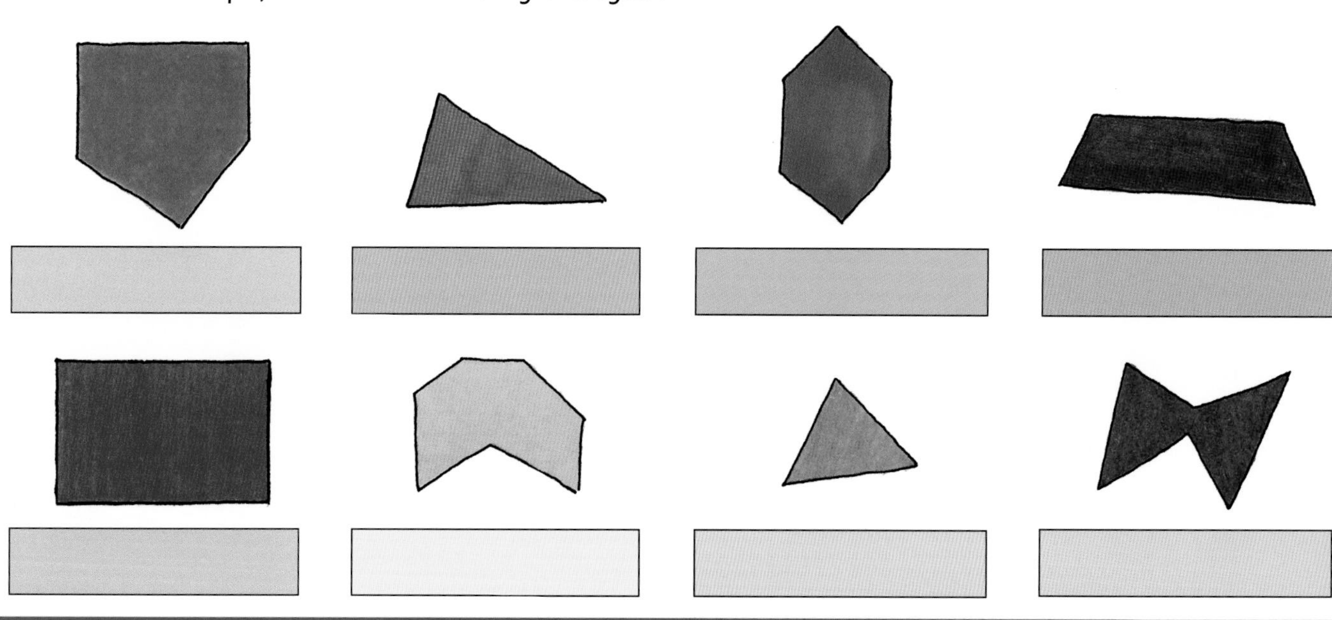

Challenge

Draw three regular polygons on this grid. Label them.

Number sequences

Look and learn

A **sequence** is usually a list of numbers in a pattern.

$1 \xrightarrow{+3} 4 \xrightarrow{+3} 7 \xrightarrow{+3} 10$

The pattern or rule is **+ 3**.

$61 \xrightarrow{-2} 59 \xrightarrow{-2} 57 \xrightarrow{-2} 55$

The pattern or rule is **− 2**.

Practice

Continue these sequences, then write the rule.

18 22 26 30 ....

The rule is:

59 52 45 38 ....

The rule is:

279 277 275 273 ....

The rule is:

71 76 81 86 ....

The rule is:

Write the missing numbers in the sequences.

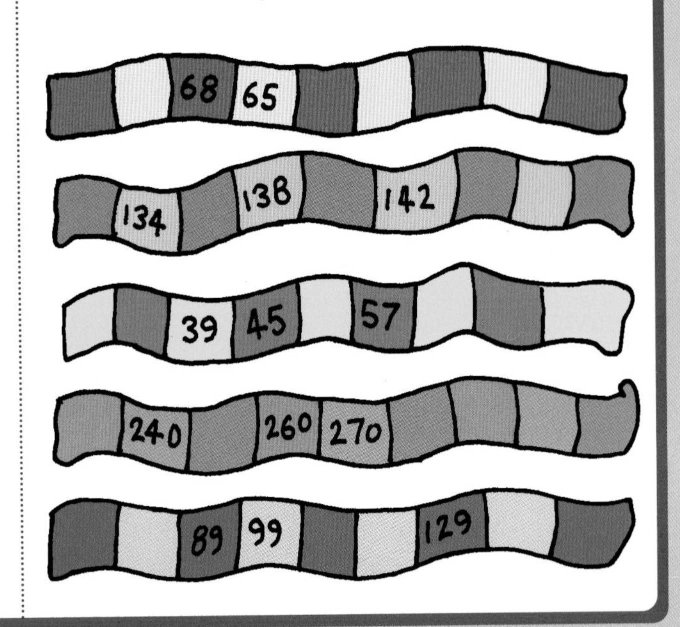

Challenge

Some sequences include **negative numbers**. Write the missing numbers on these number lines.

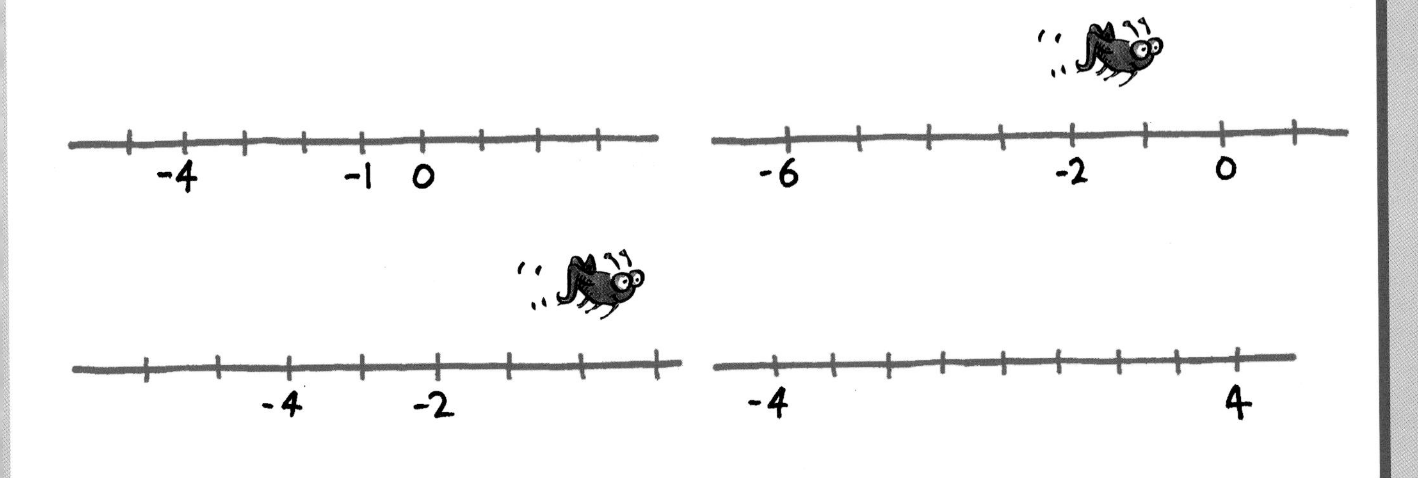

Multiplication tables

Look and learn

Learn your 2, 3, 4, 5, 6 and 10 times tables.

Quick tip

4x table is double the 2x table ⟶ 8 x 2 = 16
8 x 4 = 32

Quick tip

6x table is double the 3x table ⟶ 7 x 3 = 21
7 x 6 = 42

3 x 8 is the same as 8 x 3. It doesn't matter which way round you multiply.

Practice

Answer these. Time yourself. Try and beat your time.

3 x 4 =	5 x 7 =	8 x 2 =
5 x 5 =	6 x 3 =	6 x 4 =
2 x 7 =	8 x 4 =	10 x 7 =
10 x 0 =	10 x 6 =	4 x 8 =
8 x 3 =	9 x 3 =	7 x 6 =
9 x 2 =	4 x 7 =	9 x 5 =
4 x 4 =	6 x 6 =	6 x 9 =
0 x 6 =	9 x 10 =	5 x 8 =

Try to learn the ones you were unsure of.

Challenge

Fill in the missing numbers.

6 x ☐ = 24	☐ x 3 = 21	4 x ☐ = 28	☐ x 5 = 45
☐ x 6 = 6	9 x ☐ = 18	☐ x 5 = 30	4 x ☐ = 24
5 x ☐ = 25	☐ x 4 = 32	6 x ☐ = 36	☐ x 4 = 36

Money

Look and learn

It is useful to know how to change pounds into pence, and vice versa.

£1 = 100p

£1.50 = 150p
£0.85 = 85p
£2.70 = 270p
£4.37 = 437p

Practice

Convert these to pence.

£1.80 =

£2.95 =

£8.32 =

£4.07 =

£10.30 =

£6.05 =

£12.09 =

Convert these to pounds.

840p =

74p =

207p =

319p =

502p =

1045p =

1230p =

Total these.

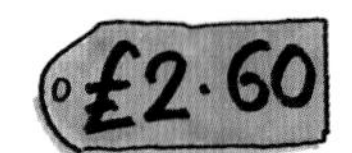

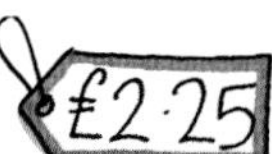

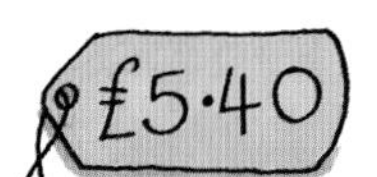

Challenge

Which coins would you need to buy . . .

spring rolls?

chop suey?

prawn crackers?

rice?

You have £10 to spend. Choose what you would like from the menu and write the total.

Food	Price
Total	

Fractions (1)

Look and learn

Fractions which are the same value are called **equivalent fractions**.

$\frac{2}{4}$ is the same as $\frac{1}{2}$

$\frac{1}{3}$ is the same as $\frac{2}{6}$

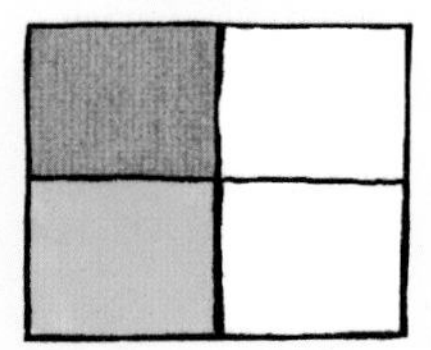 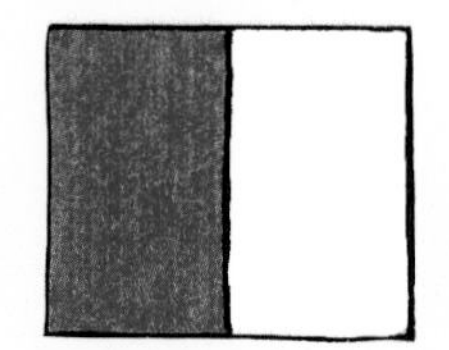 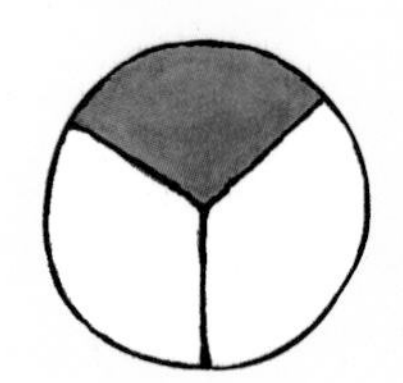 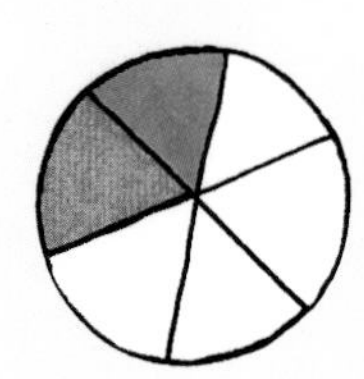

Practice

Write the fractions coloured.

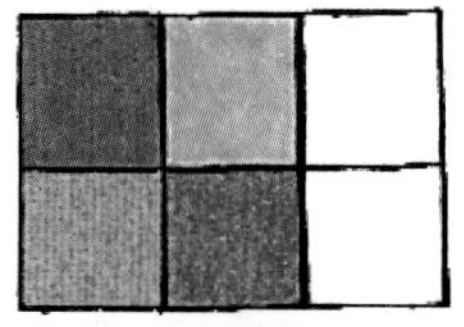

$\frac{\square}{6} = \frac{\square}{3}$

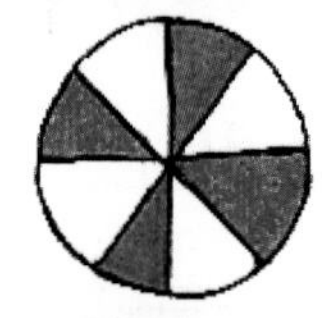

$\frac{\square}{8} = \frac{\square}{2}$

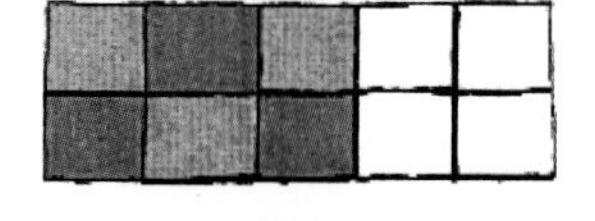

$\frac{\square}{10} = \frac{\square}{5}$

$\frac{\square}{8} = \frac{\square}{4}$

Complete these fractions.

$\frac{3}{4} = \frac{6}{\square}$ $\qquad \frac{4}{\square} = \frac{8}{10}$

$\frac{1}{2} = \frac{3}{\square}$ $\qquad \frac{1}{5} = \frac{2}{\square}$

$\frac{\square}{6} = \frac{1}{3}$ $\qquad \frac{\square}{10} = \frac{1}{2}$

$\frac{2}{\square} = \frac{1}{4}$ $\qquad \frac{1}{\square} = \frac{3}{12}$

Challenge

Write these fractions in order, starting with the smallest.

$\frac{2}{3}$ $\quad \frac{3}{5}$ $\quad \frac{1}{2}$ $\quad \frac{1}{10}$ $\quad \frac{2}{10}$ $\quad \frac{3}{4}$ $\quad \frac{1}{4}$ $\quad \frac{9}{10}$

    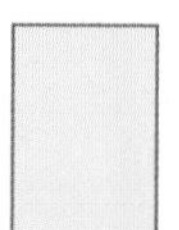 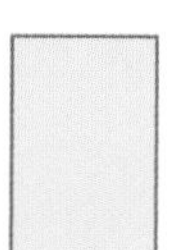 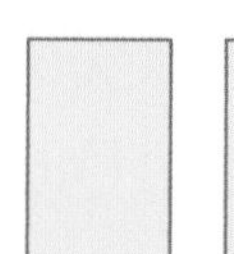

smallest — largest

Time

Look and learn

Mornings and afternoons are shown by **am** and **pm**.

7.25 am ⟶ this is in the morning.

7.25 pm ⟶ this is in the evening.

There are : 60 minutes in 1 hour,
24 hours in 1 day.

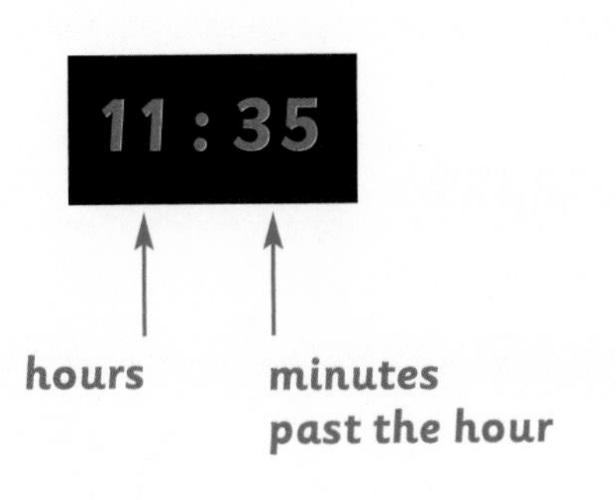

Practice

Write the times shown on each clock.

  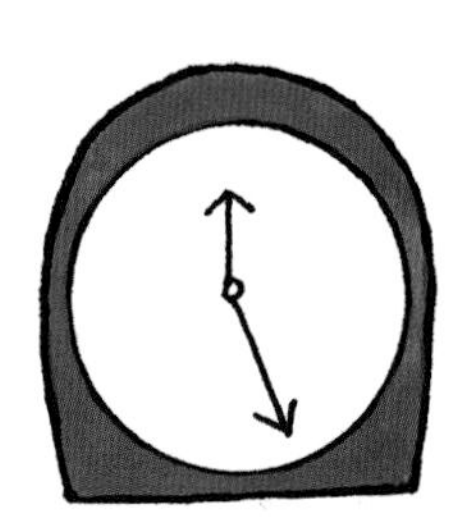 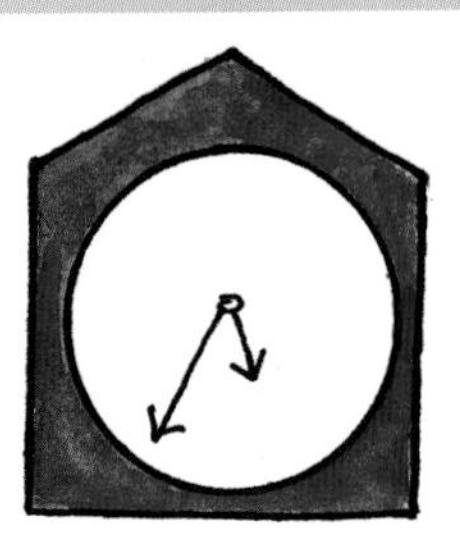

Draw the hands on these clocks.

8 : 23 | 9 : 47 | 10 : 06 | 4 : 52

Challenge

This timetable shows the times of buses:

7 : 40 am	**8 : 15 am**	**9 : 20 am**	**10 : 50 am**	**11 : 40 am**
2 : 10 pm	**4 : 30 pm**	**5 : 10 pm**	**6 : 30 pm**	**8 : 00 pm**

If you are at a bus stop at these times, how long will you have to wait?

a)
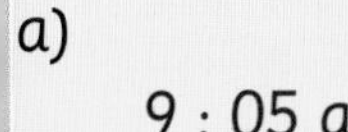  

9 : 05 am = ☐ minutes 11 : 15 am = ☐ minutes 5 : 05 pm = ☐ minutes

b)

10 : 35 am = ☐ minutes 7 : 40 pm = ☐ minutes 4 : 45 pm = ☐ minutes

Look and learn

Pictograms are symbols used to show numbers.

Key:
= 5 birds
= between 1 and 4 birds

8–9 am	
9–10 am	
10–11 am	
11–12 pm	
12–1 pm	
1–2 pm	
2–3 pm	
3–4 pm	

This is a record of the number of birds seen in a garden.

Practice

1. How many birds were seen between 11:00 am and 12:00 pm?

2. Approximately how many birds were seen between 12:00 and 1:00 pm?

3. Which was the best time to see the most birds?

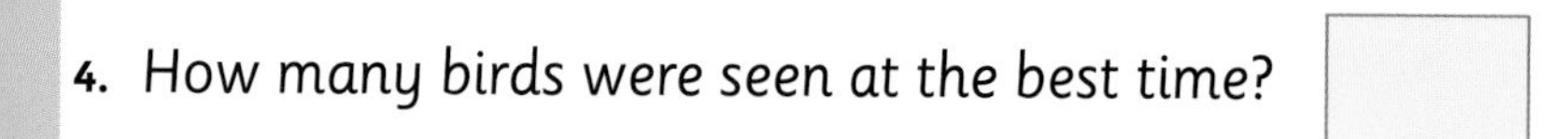

4. How many birds were seen at the best time?

5. At what time were five birds seen?

6. At what time were approximately 13 birds seen?

7. 17 birds were seen between 3:00 pm and 4:00 pm. Complete the chart above.

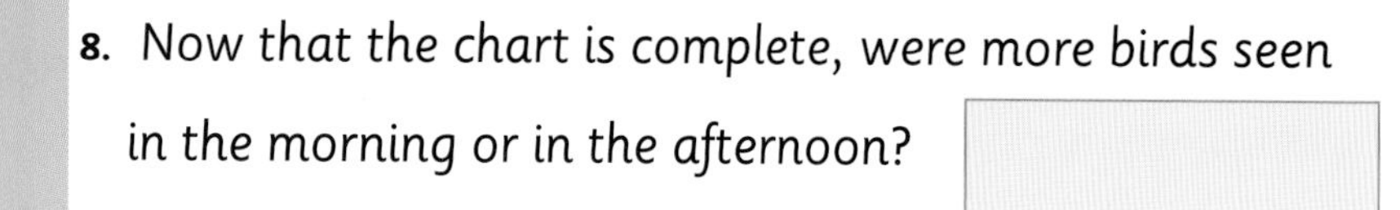

8. Now that the chart is complete, were more birds seen in the morning or in the afternoon?

9. Approximately how many birds were seen altogether?

Multiplying and dividing by 10

Look and learn

To multiply by 10, move all the digits to the left. The empty place is filled by a zero.

75 x 10 =

750

To divide by 10, move all the digits one place to the right.

230 ÷ 10 =

23

Practice

Multiply each of these numbers by 10.

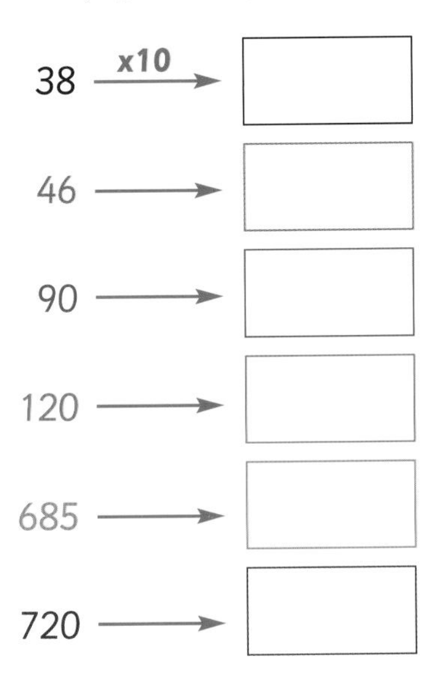

38	x10 →	
46	→	
90	→	
120	→	
685	→	
720	→	

Divide each of these numbers by 10.

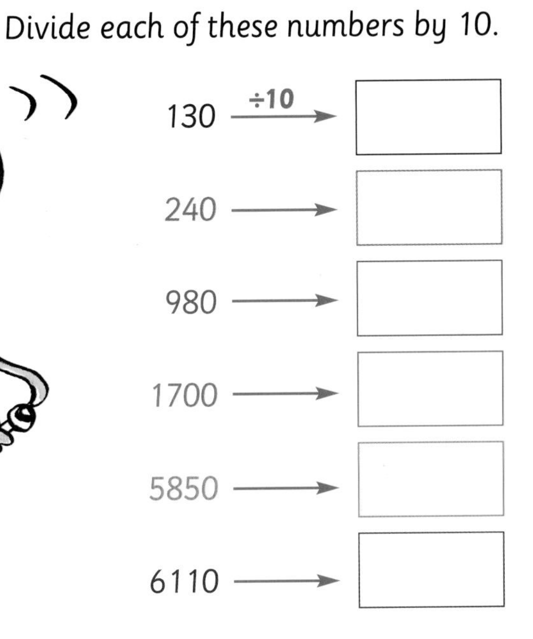

130	÷10 →	
240	→	
980	→	
1700	→	
5850	→	
6110	→	

Challenge

Write the missing numbers.

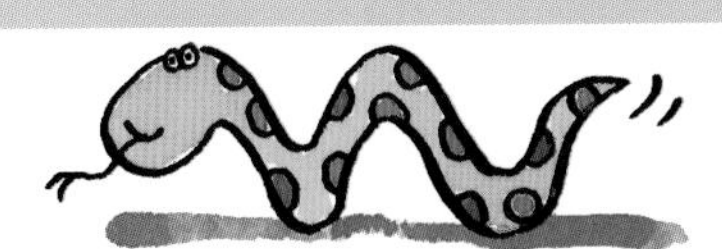

38 x ☐ = 380

☐ x 10 = 2570

☐ ÷ 10 = 600

☐ ÷ 10 = 17

8110 ÷ 10 = ☐

481 x 10 = ☐

480 ÷ 10 = ☐

6380 ÷ ☐ = 638

☐ x 10 = 3000

Addition

Look and learn

There are lots of ways to add up numbers, for example: 39 + 26

40 and 26 is 66, take one away = 65

39 add 20 is 59 add 6 = 65

30 add 20 is 50, 9 add 6 is 15, 50 add 15 = 65

9 add 6 is 15, 30 add 20 is 50, 15 add 50 = 65

Practice

Use your own methods to add these numbers in your head.

41 + 30 = ☐	35 + 28 = ☐	4 + 8 + 13 = ☐
60 + 35 = ☐	42 + 36 = ☐	9 + 3 + 7 = ☐
47 + 50 = ☐	26 + 41 = ☐	14 + 11 + 6 = ☐
40 + 46 = ☐	39 + 28 = ☐	8 + 15 + 2 = ☐
70 + 48 = ☐	45 + 38 = ☐	12 + 10 + 19 = ☐
39 + 80 = ☐	29 + 47 = ☐	18 + 5 + 13 = ☐

Challenge

Answer these.

482	279	391	285	574
+ 57	+ 46	+ 36	+ 63	+ 87
___	___	___	___	___

Money: adding coins

Look and learn

When adding coins, start with the highest value coins to make it easier.

£1.20 + 20p + 10p + 5p + 2p + 1p = £1.58

Practice

Which coins would you use to buy these books?

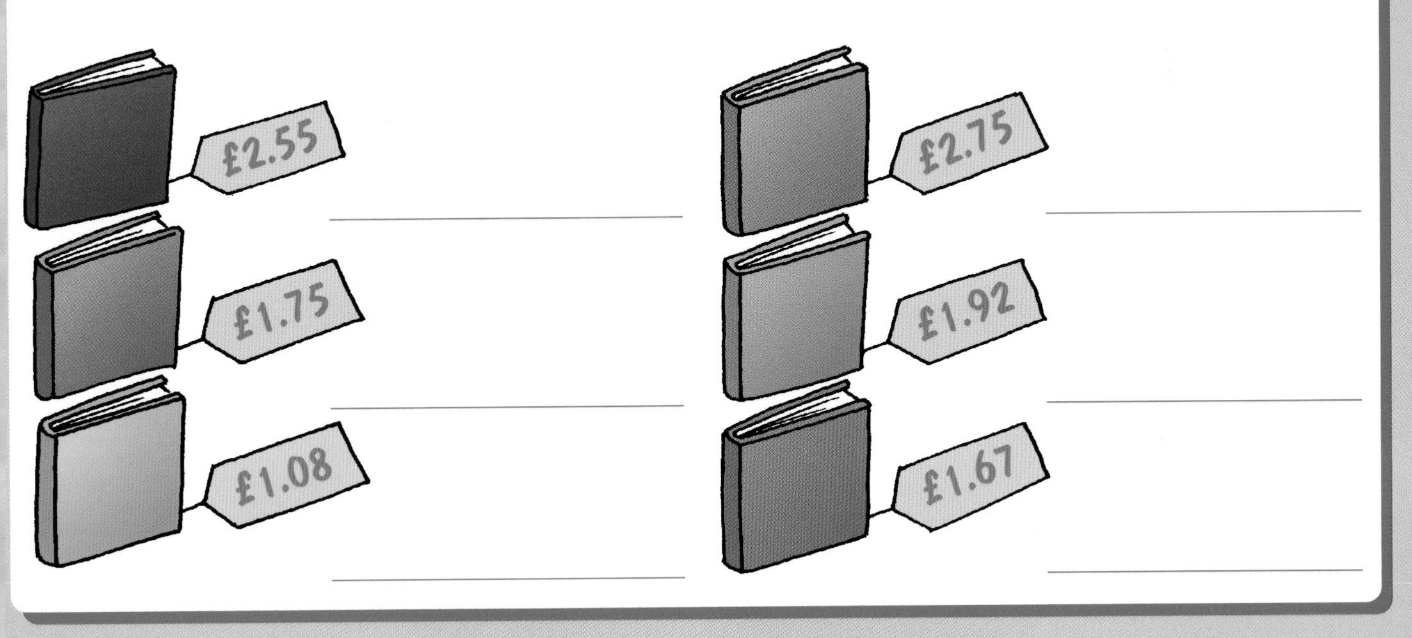

Challenge

Use these coins to make £5 in 5 different ways.

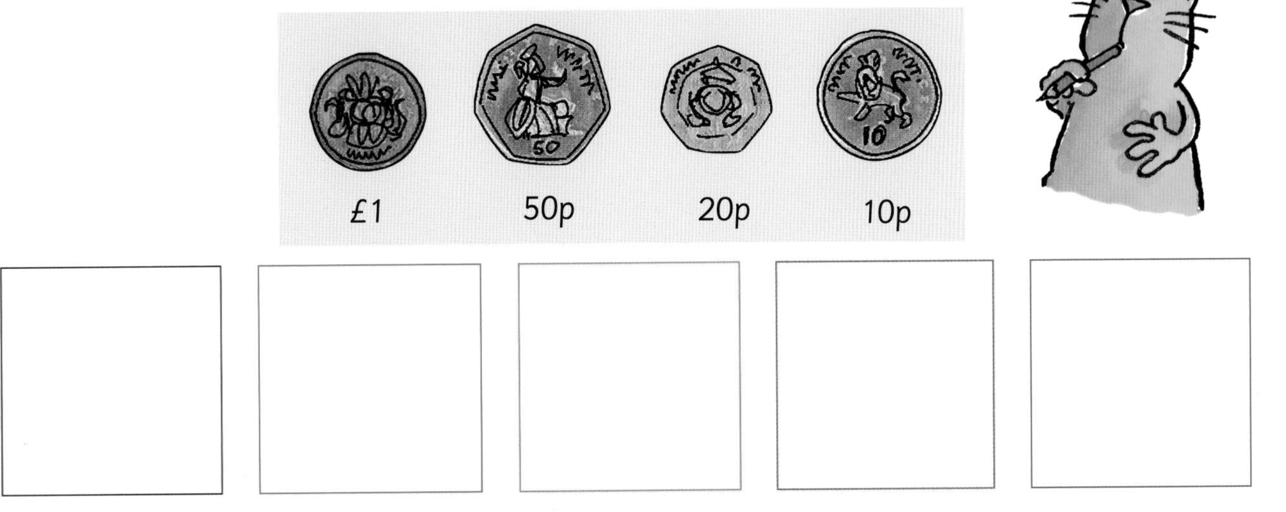

Measures problems

Look and learn

When you do word problems read the question carefully, then work out what calculation you need to do.

A shoe weighs 450g. What is the weight of two shoes?

calculation = 450 x 2

answer = 900g

Practice

1. 14 sticks, 10cm in length, are laid end to end. What is the total length?
2. A bottle holds 600ml of oil. How many 15ml spoonfuls are in a bottle?
3. A jug holds 3 litres. A glass holds 250ml. How many glasses will the jug fill?
4. A car travels 48km each day. How far will it travel in 5 days?
5. Callum has 90g of butter. He uses 35g for a recipe. How much butter is left?

Challenge

This is a chocolate cake recipe for 4 people.

Write a chocolate cake recipe for 12 people.

3D shapes

Look and learn

3D shapes are sometimes called **solid shapes**.
These are the parts of a 3 dimensional shape.

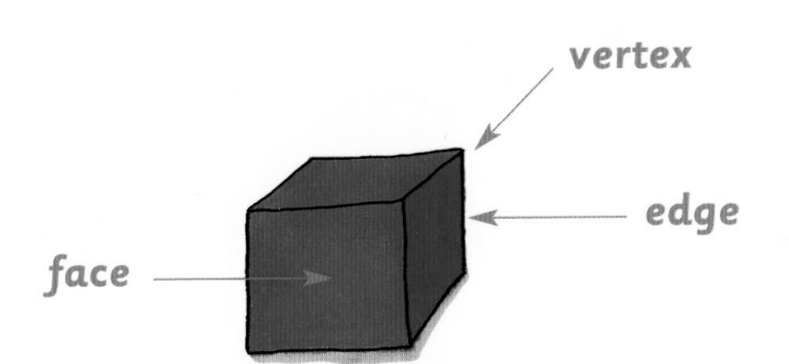

A cube has:
8 corners (vertices)
12 edges
6 faces

Practice

Name each shape. Choose the right word from the box.

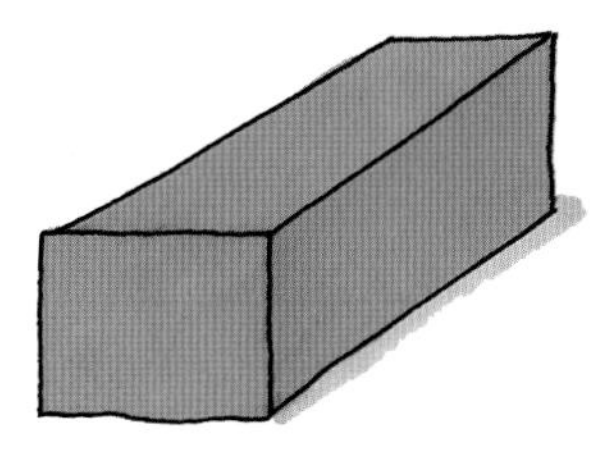

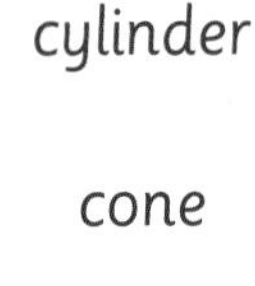

cylinder
cone
cube
pyramid
sphere
cuboid

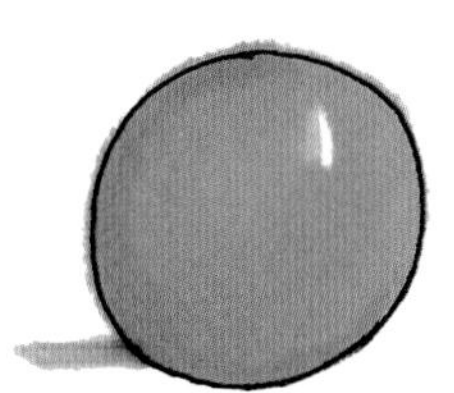
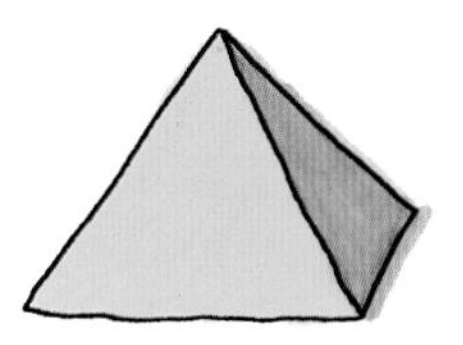

Challenge

Name these shapes.

1. I am completely curved. What am I?

2. I have 6 square faces. What am I?

3. I have 1 square and 4 triangular faces. What am I?

4. I have 2 square and 4 rectangular faces. What am I?

Number patterns on grids

Challenge

Follow the instructions for each pair of grids. Look for any patterns.

- Colour 3.
- Count on 3 and colour 6.
- Count on 3 and colour 9.
- Continue the pattern.

1	2	3	4	5	6
7	8	9	10	11	12
13	14	15	16	17	18
19	20	21	22	23	24
25	26	27	28	29	30
31	32	33	34	35	36

1	2	3	4	5	6	7
8	9	10	11	12	13	14
15	16	17	18	19	20	21
22	23	24	25	26	27	28
29	30	31	32	33	34	35
36	37	38	39	40	41	42
43	44	45	46	47	48	49

- Colour 2.
- Count on 2 and colour 4.
- Count on 2 and colour 6.
- Continue the pattern.

1	2	3	4	5	6
7	8	9	10	11	12
13	14	15	16	17	18
19	20	21	22	23	24
25	26	27	28	29	30
31	32	33	34	35	36

1	2	3	4	5	6	7
8	9	10	11	12	13	14
15	16	17	18	19	20	21
22	23	24	25	26	27	28
29	30	31	32	33	34	35
36	37	38	39	40	41	42
43	44	45	46	47	48	49

- Choose a starting number.
- Count on in threes.
- Colour a pattern on the grid.

1	2	3	4	5	6	7	8
9	10	11	12	13	14	15	16
17	18	19	20	21	22	23	24
25	26	27	28	29	30	31	32
33	34	35	36	37	38	39	40
41	42	43	44	45	46	47	48
49	50	51	52	53	54	55	56
57	58	59	60	61	62	63	64

Division

Look and learn

Use division facts to work out and check multiplication questions:

To check $8 \times 3 = 24$

try division

$24 \div 8 = 3$ $24 \div 3 = 8$

If a number cannot be divided exactly, it leaves a **remainder**.

$31 \div 5 = 6$ remainder $= 1$

Practice

Answer these.

$24 \div 4 =$	$80 \div 10 =$
$30 \div 3 =$	$21 \div 3 =$
$36 \div 4 =$	$28 \div 2 =$
$55 \div 5 =$	$130 \div 10 =$
$60 \div 2 =$	$48 \div 4 =$
$32 \div 4 =$	$90 \div 3 =$
$60 \div 5 =$	$200 \div 10 =$

Now try these.

$32 \div 3 =$		remainder
$47 \div 5 =$		remainder
$25 \div 3 =$		remainder
$86 \div 10 =$		remainder
$41 \div 2 =$		remainder
$50 \div 4 =$		remainder
$39 \div 4 =$		remainder

Challenge

Answer these. Check that the answers make sense.

1. Daniel has £29. Aquarium tickets cost £4. How many tickets can he buy?

2. Gemma has a 32cm length of string. She wants 10cm lengths. How many will she have.

3. 68 people are going on a trip. Minibuses can take 10 people. How many minibuses will be needed?

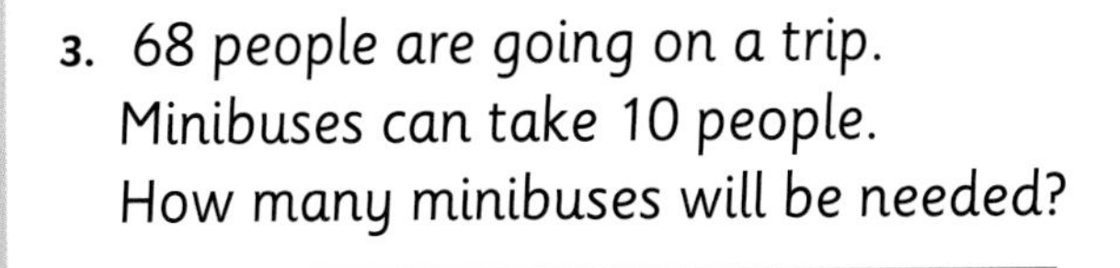

4. 63 pieces of paper are put into folders which hold 5 pieces of paper each. How many folders are needed?

Money problems (1)

Look and learn

When finding the difference between two amounts, count on from the lower amount.

The difference between £1.70 and £3.60 is £1.90 (30p + £1 + 60p).

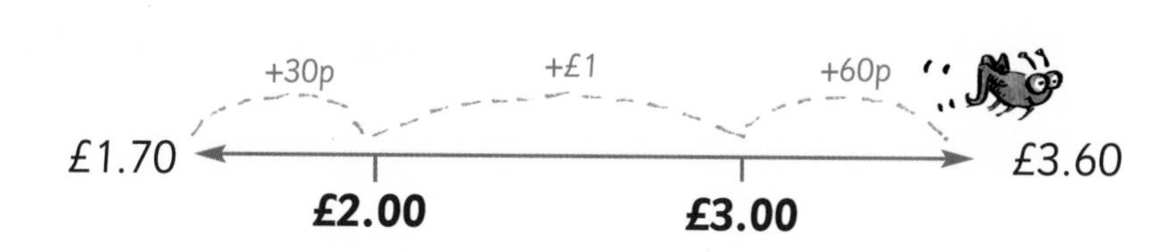

Practice

Find the difference between these prices.

difference 

difference 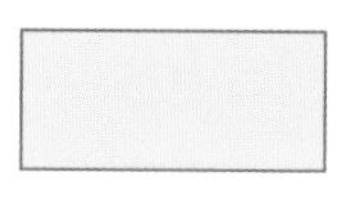

difference 

difference

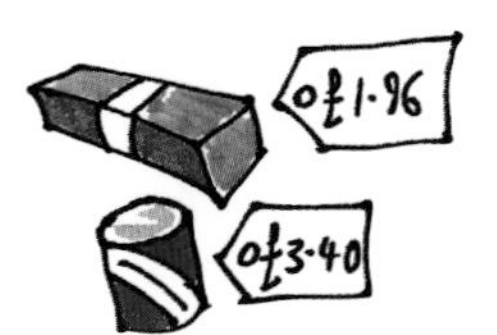

difference

difference 

Challenge

Answer these problems.

A cake costs 85p.

- How many can you buy for £4?
- What change would you get? 

A sandwich costs £1.35.

- What is the cost of 2 sandwiches?
- How much change would there be from £5?

Fractions (2)

Look and learn

It is useful to remember how to work out fractions.

$\frac{1}{4}$ of 20 is the same as $20 \div 4 = 5$

$\frac{1}{3}$ of 18 is the same as $18 \div 3 = 6$

Practice

Find $\frac{1}{4}$ of:	Find $\frac{1}{3}$ of:	Find $\frac{1}{5}$ of:
12 → ◯	15 → ◯	10 → ◯
40 → ◯	24 → ◯	45 → ◯
16 → ◯	30 → ◯	15 → ◯
8 → ◯	21 → ◯	25 → ◯
32 → ◯	9 → ◯	40 → ◯
24 → ◯	12 → ◯	50 → ◯

Challenge

Divide each grid into shapes. Make some interesting patterns. Colour each grid as shown.

$\frac{1}{3}$ → red

$\frac{1}{2}$ → blue

$\frac{1}{6}$ → yellow

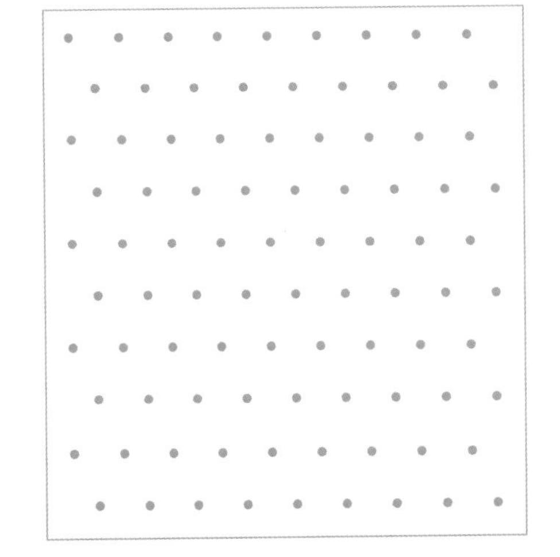

Challenge

The same numbers have been put into each area on these diagrams. Compare them.

Venn diagram

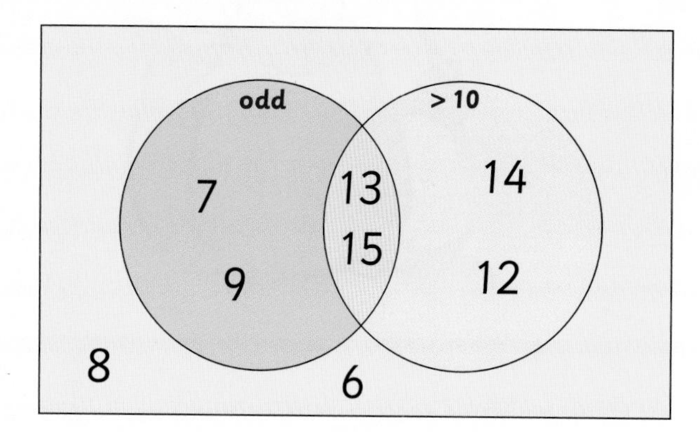

Carroll diagram

	odd	not odd
> 10	13, 15	14, 12
not > 10	7, 9	8, 6

Write these numbers in the correct places on each of these diagrams.

16 27 1 32 28 9 38 17 47 12 21 2 19 35 18 50

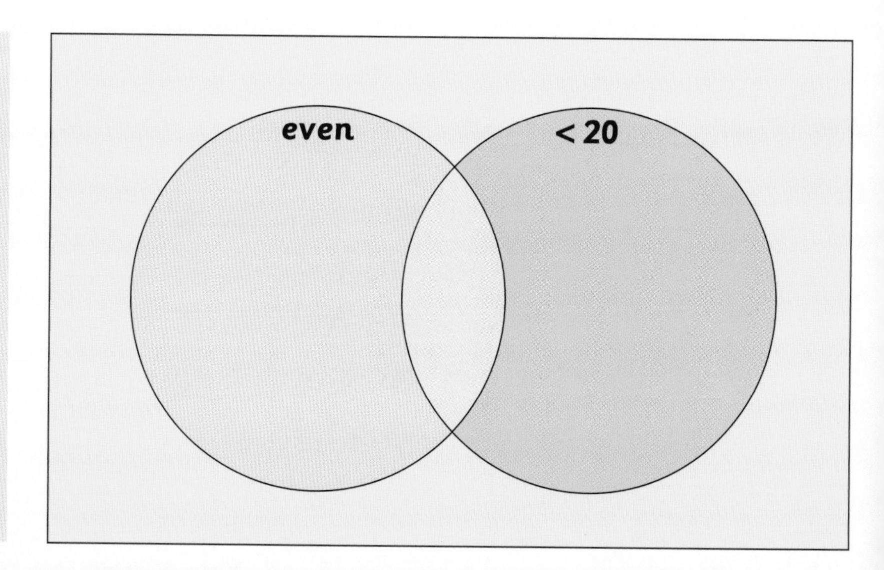

	even	not even
< 20		
not < 20		

Now write some of your own numbers on each diagram.

Place value (2)

Look and learn

To help work out the order of numbers, you can write them in a list, lining up the units columns:

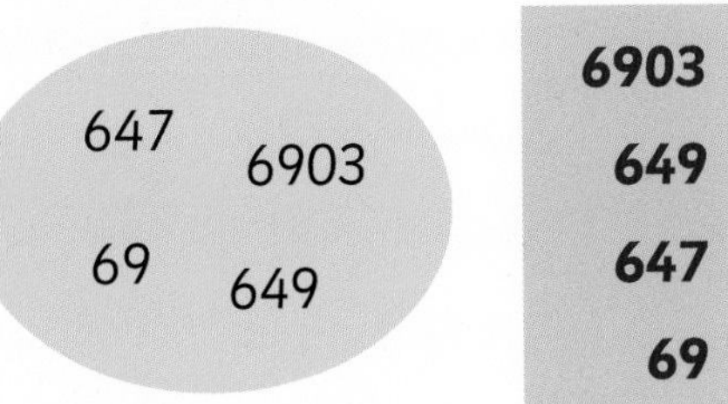

6903
649
647
69

We commonly use the symbols > and < to show the order of numbers.

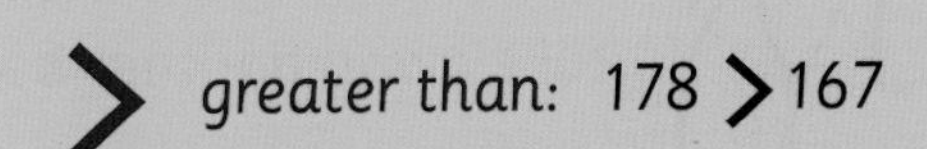

< smaller than: 242 < 442

Practice

Write the signs > or < for each pair of numbers.

164	☐	106	297	☐	299
4328	☐	4483	6100	☐	6010
2944	☐	2490	3926	☐	3990
7105	☐	7098	2761	☐	2763

Try these.

2810	☐	3629	☐	3062
4310	☐	7098	☐	4873

Write these numbers in order, starting with the smallest.

4600 3920 450 3965 3956 493 4613 4070

Challenge

Estimate the numbers shown on the line.

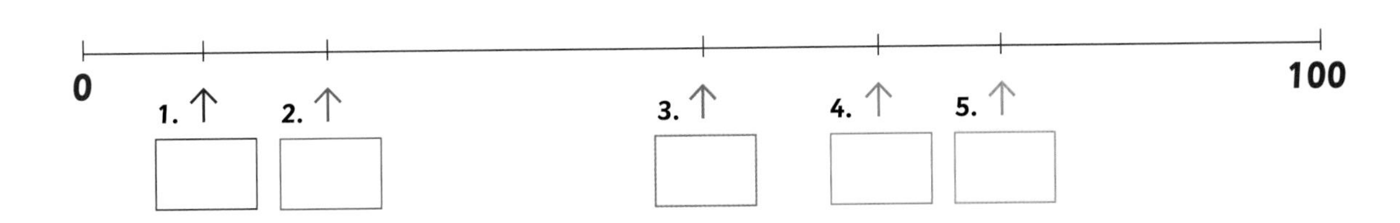

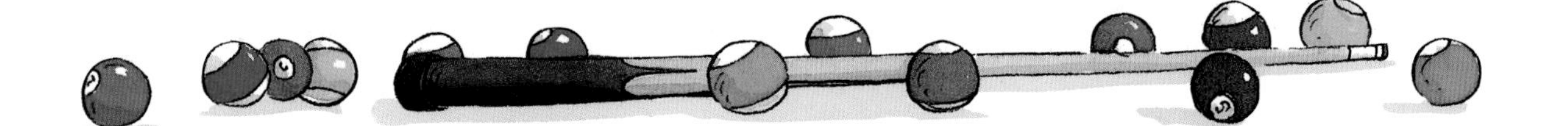

Subtraction

Look and learn

There are lots of ways to take one number from another, for example: **43 – 28**

43 take away 20 is 23,
take away another 8 = 15

28 on to 30 is 2,
30 on to 43 is 13,
add 2 = 15

43 take away 30 is 13,
add 2 = 15

Practice

Use your own methods to subtract these numbers in your head.

36 – 23 = ☐	53 – 38 = ☐	600 – 7 = ☐
54 – 32 = ☐	46 – 29 = ☐	400 – 8 = ☐
24 – 17 = ☐	64 – 23 = ☐	705 – 9 = ☐
35 – 19 = ☐	58 – 39 = ☐	503 – 7 = ☐
26 – 18 = ☐	52 – 47 = ☐	607 – 8 = ☐
43 – 27 = ☐	48 – 19 = ☐	404 – 9 = ☐

Challenge

Answer these.

$$\begin{array}{r} 347 \\ -\ \ 63 \\ \hline \\ \hline \end{array} \quad \begin{array}{r} 408 \\ -\ \ 37 \\ \hline \\ \hline \end{array} \quad \begin{array}{r} 516 \\ -\ \ 47 \\ \hline \\ \hline \end{array} \quad \begin{array}{r} 637 \\ -\ \ 44 \\ \hline \\ \hline \end{array} \quad \begin{array}{r} 576 \\ -\ \ 59 \\ \hline \\ \hline \end{array}$$

Area

Look and learn

For shapes with straight sides, count $\frac{1}{2}$ squares.

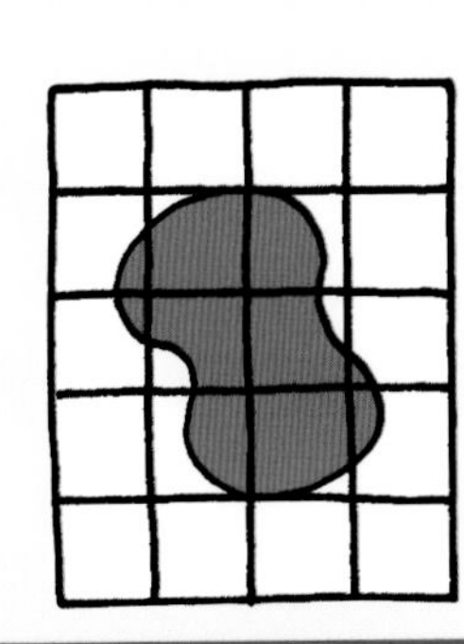

To work out the area of an irregular shape count the whole squares.

$\frac{1}{2}$ or more squares count as whole squares.

Ignore squares less than $\frac{1}{2}$.

Practice

Work out the approximate areas of these shapes.

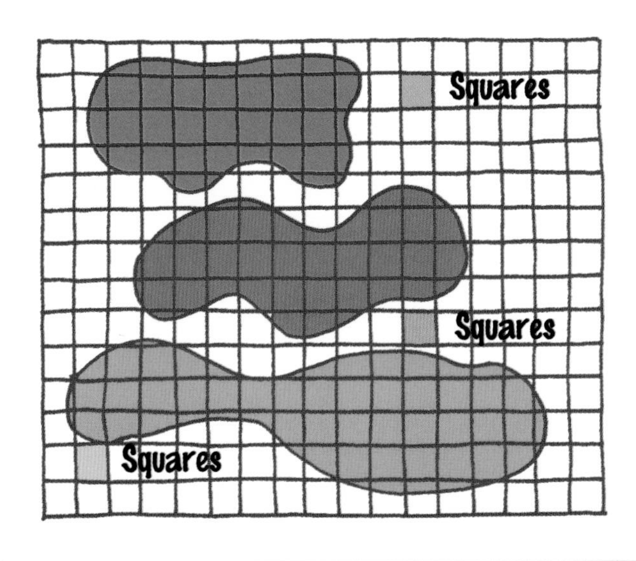

Work out the areas of these shapes.

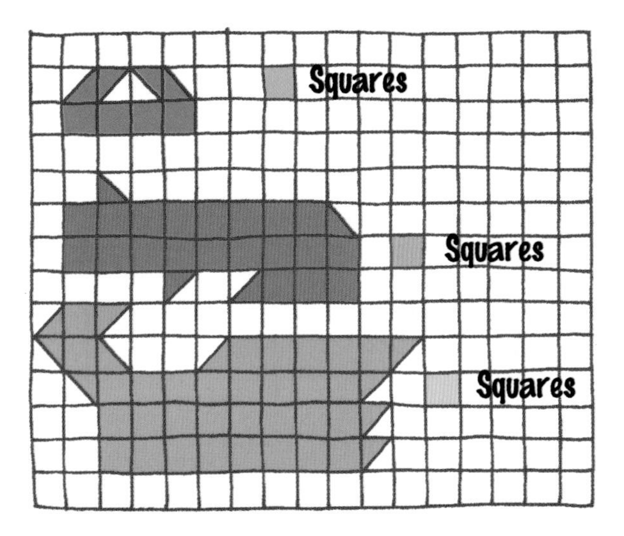

Challenge

Draw shapes with an area of 6 squares. How many different shapes can you make?

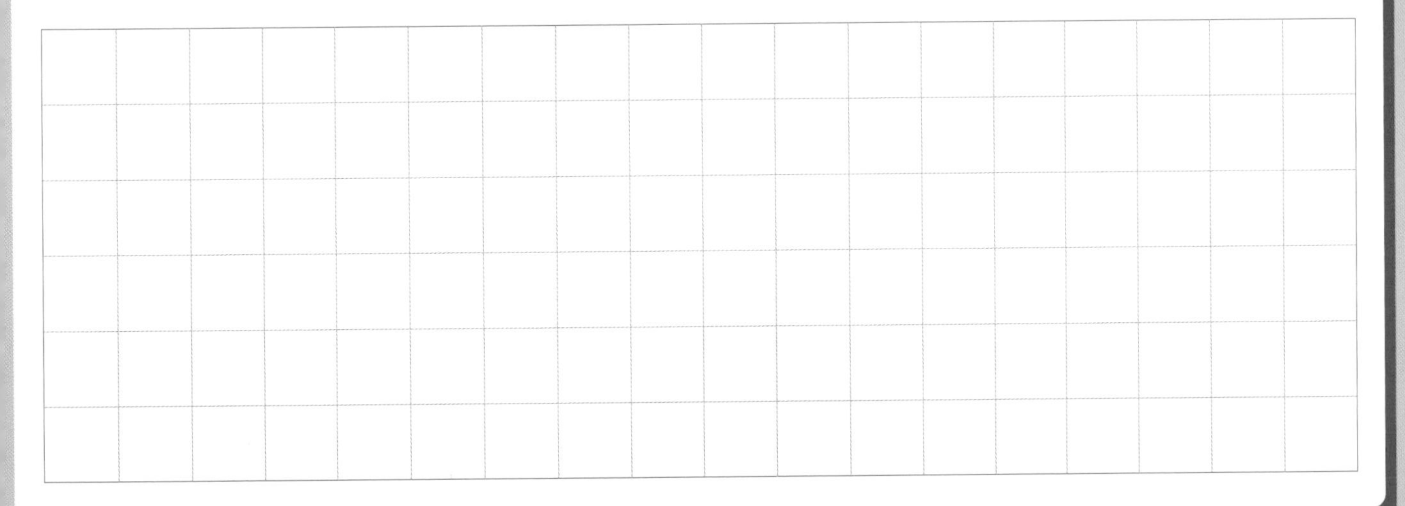

Shape: symmetry

Look and learn

A shape is **symmetrical** if both sides are exactly the same when a mirror line is drawn.

A shape reflected in a mirror.

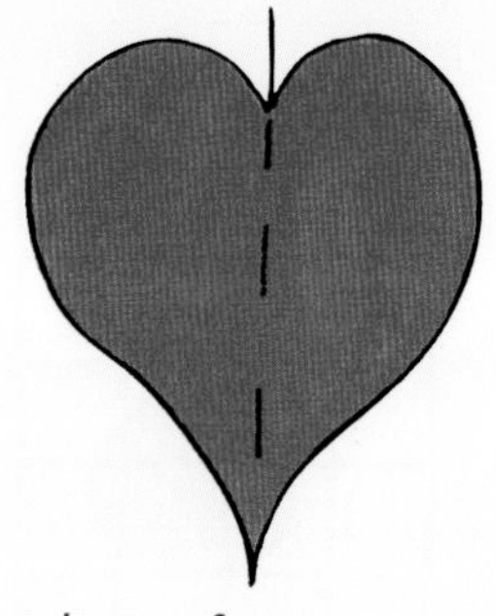

1 line of symmetry

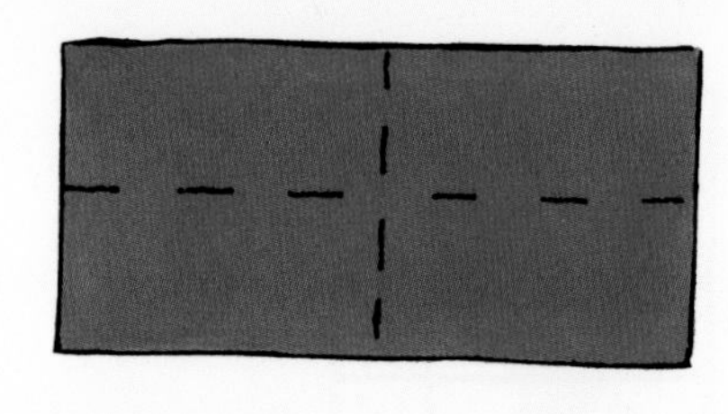

2 lines of symmetry

Practice

Draw the reflection of each shape. Colour the shapes.

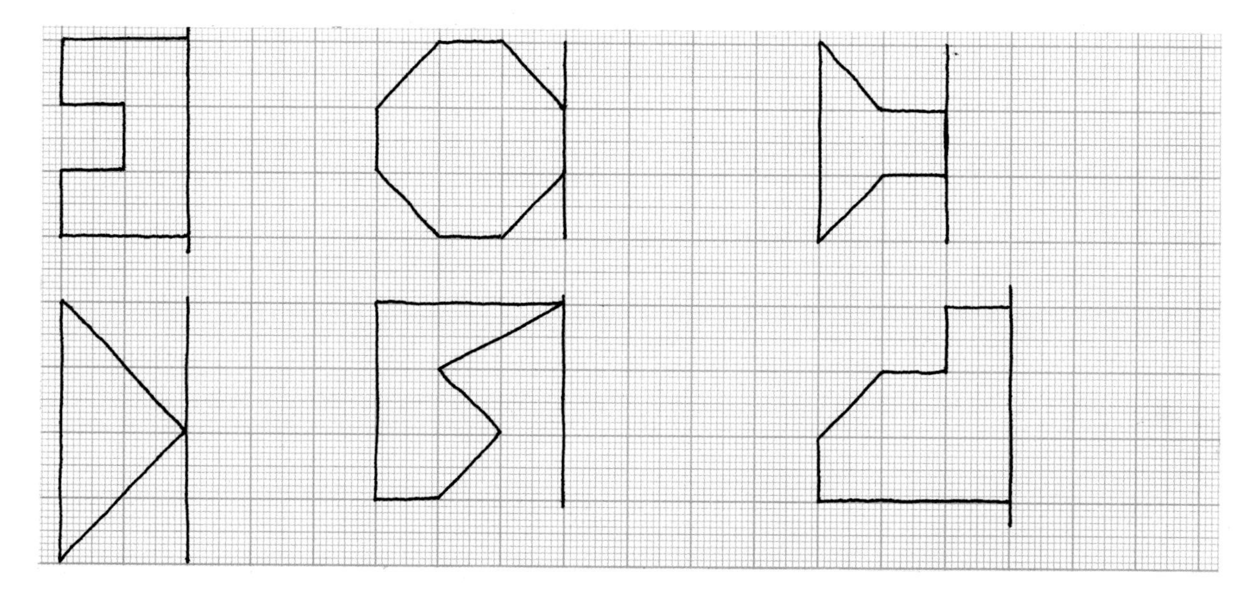

Challenge

Draw lines of symmetry on these shapes.

Multiples

Look and learn

Multiples of 2 are: 2, 4, 6, 8, 10, 12 . . . and so on.

Multiples of 3 are: 3, 6, 9, 12, 15, 18 . . . and so on.

Multiples of a number do not come to an end at ×10, they go on and on . . . so, 48, 92, 146, 200 are all multiples of 2.

Practice

Write these numbers in the correct boxes. Some of them will belong in more than one box.

48 56 100 39 86 52 82

42 63 85 70 115 60 65

multiples of 2	multiples of 3	multiples of 4	multiples of 5

Challenge

- Colour all the multiples of 2 in yellow.
- Circle the multiples of 5.
- Write the multiples of 10 in the box below.

1	2	3	4	5	6	7	8	9	10
11	12	13	14	15	16	17	18	19	20
21	22	23	24	25	26	27	28	29	30
31	32	33	34	35	36	37	38	39	40
41	42	43	44	45	46	47	48	49	50
51	52	53	54	55	56	57	58	59	60
61	62	63	64	65	66	67	68	69	70
71	72	73	74	75	76	77	78	79	80
81	82	83	84	85	86	87	88	89	90
91	92	93	94	95	96	97	98	99	100

Multiplication

Look and learn

It is a good idea to try to remember multiplication patterns to make calculations easier.

34×5 =

$$\begin{aligned} 30 \times 5 &= 150 \\ 4 \times 5 &= +\ 20 \\ \hline 34 \times 5 &= 170 \end{aligned}$$

=

$$\begin{array}{r} 3\ 4 \\ \times\quad 5 \\ \hline 1\ 7\ 0 \\ \hline {\scriptstyle 2} \end{array}$$

Practice

Answer these.

20 × 2 =	40 × 3 =
27 × 2 =	46 × 3 =
30 × 4 =	50 × 4 =
34 × 4 =	56 × 4 =
40 × 5 =	80 × 2 =
41 × 5 =	86 × 2 =
30 × 3 =	60 × 5 =
38 × 3 =	4 × 5 =

Now try these.

42 × 3 = ☐

51 × 2 = ☐

37 × 5 = ☐

29 × 4 = ☐

52 × 5 = ☐

33 × 4 = ☐

45 × 3 = ☐

Challenge

Answer these.

43	85	67	59	83	76
× 4	× 3	× 5	× 2	× 5	× 4
____	____	____	____	____	____

Money problems (2)

Look and learn

When working out word problems, read the question carefully to work out the calculation you need to do.

If one book costs £1.30 and another costs £2.60, how much change will you get from £5?

calculation → £1.30 + £2.60 = £3.90
£5.00 – £3.90 =

answer → £1.10

Practice

1. A bar of chocolate costs 35p. What do 4 bars cost?
2. What is the total cost of a £4.70 shirt and a £2.90 hat?
3. A jigsaw costs £8.30. It is reduced by £2.90 in a sale. What is the new price of the jigsaw?

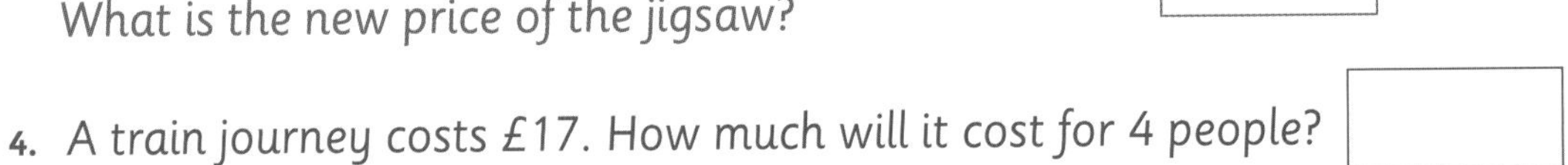

4. A train journey costs £17. How much will it cost for 4 people?
5. Sam has 84p. He spends 29p. How much does he have left?
6. Laura has two 50p coins and three 20p coins. She buys an ice-cream at £1.05. How much money does she have left?
7. A pencil costs 19p. How many can be bought for £2?

Challenge

Ben pays for a stamp with three different silver coins.
Complete the chart to show all the different totals he can make.

5p	✓			
10p	✓			
20p	✓			
50p				
total	35p			

If he was given 12p change, what would the price of the stamp be?

Decimals

Look and learn

A **decimal point** is used to separate whole numbers from fractions.

So:

$0{\cdot}1 = \frac{1}{10}$ $0{\cdot}2 = \frac{2}{10}$ $0{\cdot}5 = \frac{1}{2}$

tens	units		tenths
3	4	·	8
30	4		$\frac{8}{10}$

Practice

Change these fractions to decimals.

$\frac{3}{10} =$ ☐ $1\frac{7}{10} =$ ☐

$\frac{1}{2} =$ ☐ $3\frac{3}{10} =$ ☐

$\frac{2}{10} =$ ☐ $4\frac{1}{2} =$ ☐

$\frac{7}{10} =$ ☐ $7\frac{9}{10} =$ ☐

$\frac{9}{10} =$ ☐ $5\frac{1}{10} =$ ☐

Write these decimals on the lines.

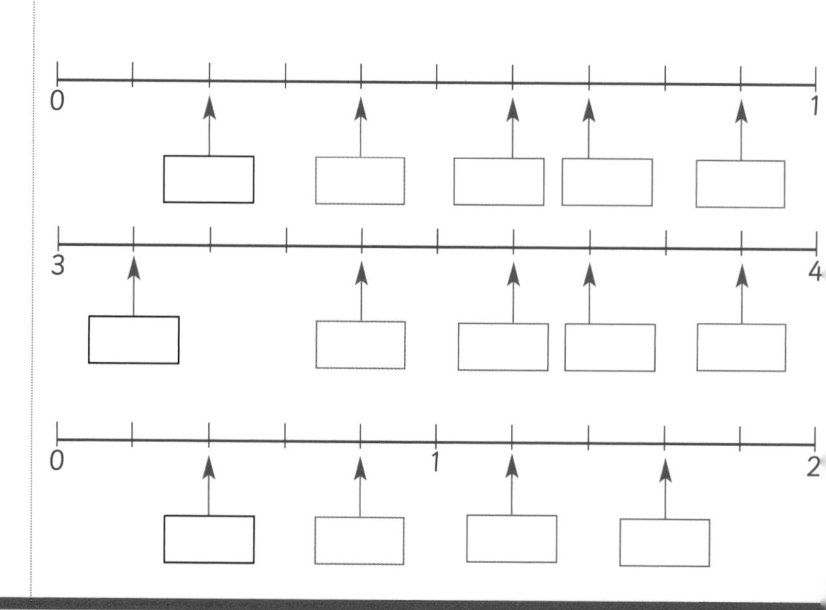

Challenge

Write these numbers in order, starting with the smallest.

1·3 3·1 3 2·8 2·4 2 2·5 1·9

Try it with these numbers.

10·9 8 8·4 8·5 1·6 1·9 10·1 7·9

Challenge

Answer these.

1. A television programme started at 6.50pm and finished at 7.45pm. How long was the programme?

2. Jonathan went to the library on Tuesday 18th May and then again two weeks later. What was the date when he went to the library the second time?

3. A cake takes 35 minutes to bake. If it went in the oven at 6.15pm, what time does it need to come out?

4. A football team kicked off at 11.45am. They played 45 minutes each way and had a 10 minute break. What time did they finish?

5. A sports shop started its sale on Saturday 3rd January. The sale finished on Saturday 7th February. How many weeks was the sale on for?

6. A train arrived at Kings Cross from Newark at 4.45pm. The journey lasted 1 hour 35 minutes. What time did the train leave Newark?

7. Kate took 2 minutes and 18 seconds to complete a race. How many seconds is this?

8. A bus takes 15 minutes between bus stops. Complete the timetable.

Church	3·05			
Green Lane			6·15	
Hospital		5·20		
Post Office				8·25

Challenge

The two graphs below show the results of a survey of lunch boxes at a school.

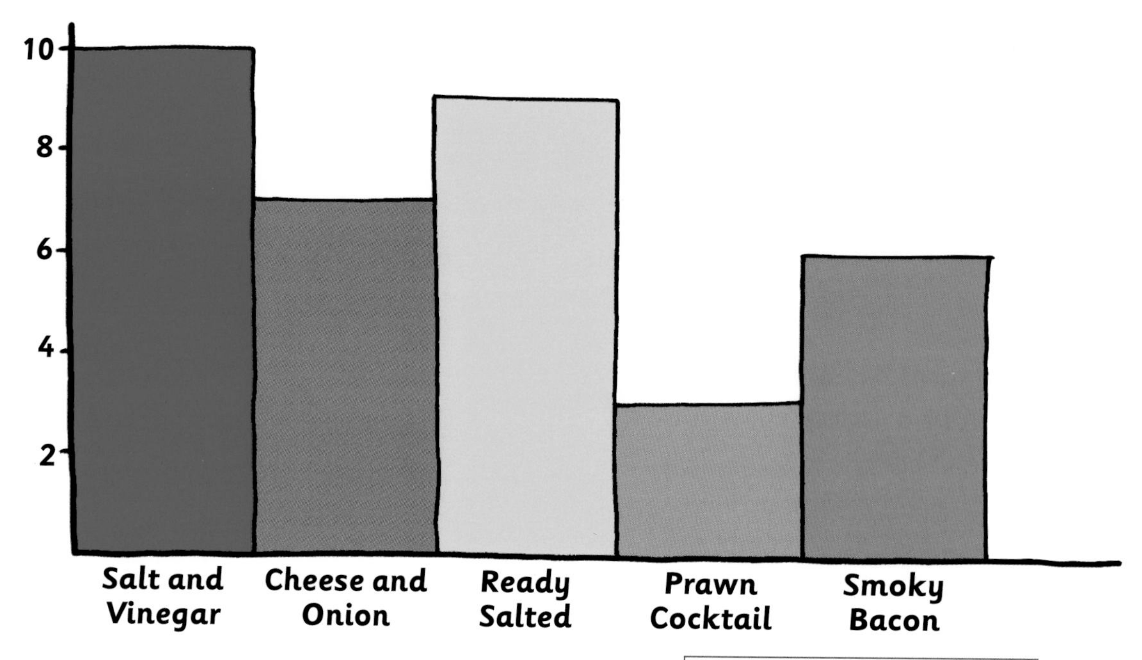

Which flavour did 9 children pack for their lunch?

How many children brought salt and vinegar crisps?

How many more children brought ready salted than prawn cocktail?

How many children brought crisps altogether?

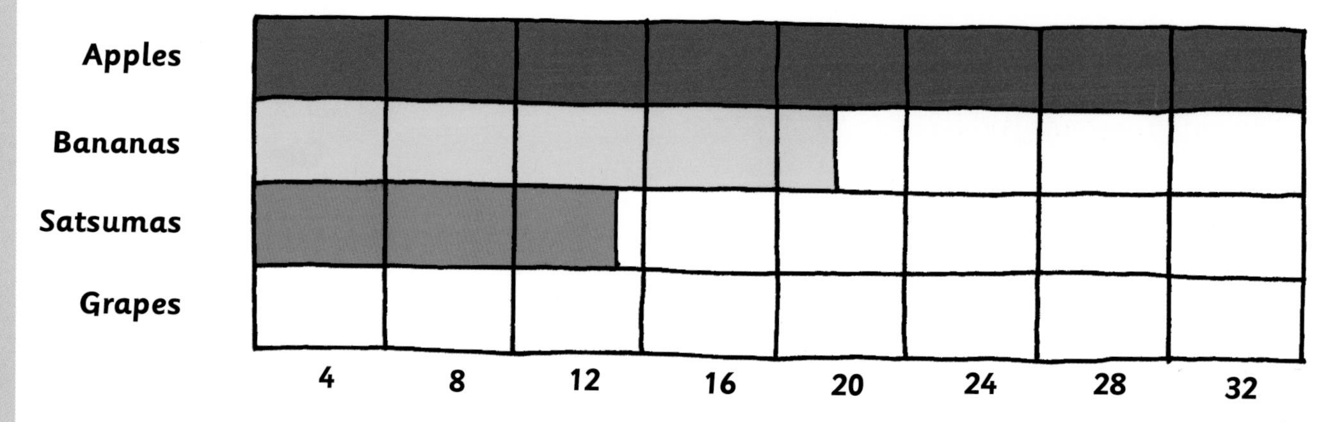

How many children brought apples?

How many more bananas than satsumas were brought?

7 children brought grapes. Draw this on the graph.

How many children brought fruit altogether?